THE BOOK OF

1 Corinthians

ONE CHAPTER A DAY

GoodMorningGirls.org

Welcome to Good Morning Girls! We are so glad you are joining us.

God created us to walk with Him, to know Him, and to be loved by Him. He is our living well, and when we drink from the water He continually provides, His living water will change the entire course of our lives.

Jesus said: "Whoever drinks of the water that I will give him will never be thirsty again. The water that I will give him will become in him a spring of water welling up to eternal life." ~ John 4:14 (ESV)

So let's begin.

The method we use here at GMG is called the **SOAK** method.

S—The S stands for *Scripture*—Read the chapter for the day. Then choose 1-2 verses and write them out word for word. (There is no right or wrong choice—just let the Holy Spirit guide you.)

O—The O stands for *Observation*—Look at the verse or verses you wrote out. Write 1 or 2 observations. What stands out to you? What do you learn about the character of God from these verses? Is there a promise, command or teaching?

A—The A stands for *Application*—Personalize the verses. What is God saying to you? How can you apply them to your life? Are there any changes you need to make or an action to take?

K—The K stands for *Kneeling in Prayer*—Pause, kneel and pray. Confess any sin God has revealed to you today. Praise God for His word. Pray the passage over your own life or someone you love. Ask God to help you live out your applications.

SOAK God's word into your heart and squeeze every bit of nourishment you can out of each day's scripture reading. Soon you will find your life transformed by the renewing of your mind!

Walk with the King!

Courtney

WomenLivingWell.org, GoodMorningGirls.org

Join the GMG Community

Share your daily SOAK on **Facebook.com/GoodMorningGirlsWLW**

Instagram: WomenLivingWell #GoodMorningGirls

GMG Bible Coloring Chart

COLORS	KEYWORDS
PURPLE	God, Jesus, Holy Spirit, Saviour, Messiah
PINK	women of the Bible, family, marriage, parenting, friendship, relationships
RED	love, kindness, mercy, compassion, peace, grace
GREEN	faith, obedience, growth, fruit, salvation, fellowship, repentance
YELLOW	worship, prayer, praise, doctrine, angels, miracles,power of God, blessings
BLUE	wisdom, teaching, instruction, commands
ORANGE	prophecy, history, times, places, kings, genealogies, people, numbers, covenants, vows, visions, oaths, future
BROWN/GRAY	Satan, sin, death, hell, evil, idols, false teachers, hypocrisy, temptation

Introduction to the Book of 1 Corinthians

Welcome to our study through the book of 1 Corinthians. This book is going to challenge us, as we cover issues that have been divisive inside the church down through the ages. Some of the scriptures we will cover have been interpreted differently by scholars and have caused denominational divisions. So, as we dig deep into God's Word together, may we seek to keep unity and love at the forefront of our study together.

The book of 1 Corinthians is a letter from Paul to the church at Corinth. Paul established the church in Corinth, but soon after his departure there were divisions, disorder, immorality, confusion and a lack of love inside the church. These internal divisions were tearing the church apart and so Paul wrote to clarify, instruct and encourage the Corinthian church.

The Purpose: Paul wrote to deal with the issues that were coming up inside the church such as immorality, lawsuits, marriage, divorce, the Lord's Supper, spiritual gifts, Christian love and the resurrection.

The Author: Paul the Apostle.

Time Period: Around 55 A.D. (Paul wrote this during his third missionary journey).

Key Verse: 1 Corinthians 10:31

> *Whatever you do, do all to the glory of God.*

The Outline:

1. Introduction (1:1-9)

2. Divisions in the Corinthian Church (1:10-4:21)

3. Immorality and Lawsuits in the Corinthian Church (5-6)

4. Marriage and Divorce (7)

5. Christian Liberties and Rights (8-10)

6. The Lord's Supper (11)

7. Spiritual Gifts (12)

8. Christian Love (13)

9. Order in the Church (14)

10. The Resurrection (15)

11. Conclusion (16)

The book of 1 Corinthians is a challenging book of the Bible to study. It is going to cause us to examine our own lives closely and change. Some of the chapters are quite long, so be sure to leave at least 20 minutes for your reading each day. I can't wait to see how God reveals himself personally to each of us, as we read the book of 1 Corinthians together, chapter by chapter. So let's get started!

Keep walking with the King!

Courtney

Paul
Short essays but they all come together
describe problem
responds problem through gospel
they are not livin their life
by the gospel

1. divisions - people surround Jesus. He's the center

2. Sex - ruined relations by sex. If you're what you do with your body - it's not up to you

3 food - meat Jewish & not Jewish

Jesus as lord
your loyalty is to jesus
love the people +
not mislead them
love is at the core
love   principle

4. praying in different languages
purpose gathering
the spirit working in everyone
its one but it has all people

Center around the gospel God is the love
5 The gathering show   the different parts
5. Jesus resurrection we believe in it because all those

Let there be no divisions among you,

be united.

1 Corinthians 1:10

Reflection Question:

Paul appealed to the church at Corinth to be united with no divisions. He wanted them to see the wisdom and greatness of Jesus' work on the cross, over the wisdom and greatness of the preachers and teachers they were following. Paul reminded them that God chose the weak, foolish, low and despised of this world, to preach the power of Christ crucified. So, when we boast, may we only boast in the Lord.

Have you ever been tempted to put the wisdom of someone you follow above the wisdom of God and his word? Have you ever divided with another believer over which preachers or teachers they listen to? While it's important that we guard against false doctrine, it is equally important that we unite around the gospel truth that we have in common. In what area of your life have you become a divider and how can you work to be more united within the family of God?

1 Corinthians 1

S—The S stands for *Scripture* 1:19 I will destroy the wisdom of the wise, the intelligence of the intelligent I will frustrate.

O—The O stands for *Observation* He wants us to see the wisdom and greatness of jesus

A—The A stands for *Application*

K—The K stands for *Kneeling in Prayer*

No eye has seen, nor ear heard,

nor the heart of man imagined,

what God has prepared for those who love him.

1 Corinthians 2:9

Reflection Question:

The rulers of this world could not understand the wisdom of God in Christ and so they crucified him. But as believers God has revealed to us, through the Holy Spirit, the wisdom of the cross. Yet, our limited minds cannot comprehend all of the blessings in store for us!

Imagine planning a surprise party for someone you love. Perhaps you would choose a place they'd like to visit, a gift they'd like to receive and their favorite foods. Now, you prepare this elaborate blessing to give them and you know they are going to thoroughly enjoy it. This is how God has prepared for us. He knows better than we do what we desire and enjoy, and we cannot even fathom what he has prepared for us. How does this truth encourage you today?

1 Corinthians 2

S—The S stands for *Scripture*

2:9
However, as it is written:

No eye has seen
no ear has heard
no mind has conceived
what God has prepared for those
who love him.

O—The O stands for *Observation*

I'm never prepared what God has in
store for me. But I know it is always
a surprise and wonderful.

A—The A stands for *Application*

Because I have come it has made
my anxiety less. Things aren't as
important than God. God is number one
and the most important to me I know he
will handle the rest.

K—The K stands for *Kneeling in Prayer*

Dear Heavenly Father,
You always give 10x more to me than I
ever thought. I have so much faith in
you, but you

The fire will test what sort of work

each one has done.

If the work survives,

he will receive a reward.

1 Corinthians 3:13 & 14

Reflection Question:

God tests our works based on what "sort" of work it is. Works that are as wood, hay and straw will burn up in the fire but works that are as gold, silver and precious stones, will be rewarded. In its context, this verse is referring to the building up of the church with truth. Those who mix in human wisdom, may make it through the fire but without rewards.

God knows our motives of the heart. It does not matter how many hours we have spent serving him by building up the church. If it was not with a right heart, right motive or right truth, it will be as though we did nothing at all. On Judgement Day, our works will be tested and only what remains will be rewarded. Evaluate the ways that you are currently serving the Lord. Will they make it through the fire? What changes do you need to make, so you can be sure that your service is honoring to the Lord?

S—The S stands for *Scripture*

O—The O stands for *Observation*

A—The A stands for *Application*

K—The K stands for *Kneeling in Prayer*

For the kingdom of God

does not consist in talk

but in power.

1 Corinthians 4:20

Reflection Question:

One of the issues in the Corinthian church was that the leaders were being prideful about their spiritual wisdom. This was causing disunity in the church. Paul straightened out their wrong way of thinking by reminding them that the kingdom of God is not just a bunch of talking heads. It's the power of Christ at work in believers' lives!

While proclaiming the gospel truth is important, living lives that reveal the transforming power of the cross, is equally important. We must be witnesses of Jesus by sharing both the gospel and what God has done in our lives. How have you experienced God's power in your life? Pray and ask God to open the door for you to share the power of the gospel with someone this week.

1 Corinthians 4

S—The S stands for *Scripture*

O—The O stands for *Observation*

A—The A stands for *Application*

K—The K stands for *Kneeling in Prayer*

For what have I to do with judging outsiders?

God judges those outside.

1 Corinthians 5:12 & 13

Reflection Question:

Sexual immorality had defiled the church in Corinth. Paul called on the church to purify itself by removing those who were sinning in arrogance, in hopes that they would become repentant. These instructions were specifically for those inside the church and it was meant to be a loving act, seeking restoration. Those outside the church were not to be judged by the church but rather left for God to be the judge.

Have you experienced the church winking at the sin of those inside the church while judging harshly those outside the church? While it may seem loving to overlook the sins of those inside the church, it hurts the holiness of the church and those participating in the sin. But we cannot hold those outside the church to the same standard. In what ways have you been too judgmental of those outside the church and how can you show more love to those who are lost in their sin?

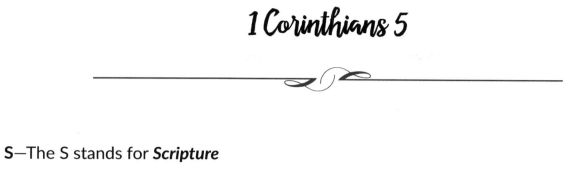

1 Corinthians 5

S—The S stands for *Scripture*

O—The O stands for *Observation*

A—The A stands for *Application*

K—The K stands for *Kneeling in Prayer*

You were bought with a price.

So glorify God in your body.

1 Corinthians 6:20

Reflection Question:

Our bodies are a temple of the Holy Spirit and a temple is a sacred place of worship. We are meant to keep our bodies pure sexually because we are not our own. We have been bought with the price of Jesus' blood. This means that we have strength that the world does not have, to remain pure.

When you use something that someone else paid for, are you more careful with it? Our bodies are on lend to us from God to be used for his glory. How can you be more careful with your body? If you have any sins that you need to repent of today, quietly pray a prayer of confession. Remember that once you confess, you are fully forgiven. (1 John 1:9)

S—The S stands for *Scripture*

O—The O stands for *Observation*

A—The A stands for *Application*

K—The K stands for *Kneeling in Prayer*

But each has his own gift from God,

one of one kind and one of another.

1 Corinthians 7:7

Reflection Question:

Everyone is either single or married. While Paul was single and saw it as good, he considered both marriage and singleness a gift from God. Each one of us is to embrace the life that the Lord has assigned to us. No one is gifted for sexual immorality. We are either to live faithfully or be celibate.

Being married has its challenges and being single has its challenges. Which are you today—single or married? How do you feel about the place God has assigned to you? How is God speaking personally to you through this chapter today?

S—The S stands for *Scripture*

O—The O stands for *Observation*

A—The A stands for *Application*

K—The K stands for *Kneeling in Prayer*

Take care that this right of yours

does not somehow become

a stumbling block to the weak.

1 Corinthians 8:9

Reflection Question:

Idol worship was a huge part of the culture in Corinth. Most of the new believers would have come out of this idolatry. So, eating meat sold in the market place, that had first been offered to idols, became an issue for the church. Many in the church most likely suffered for their choice to follow God and so their conscience would not allow them to eat the meat offered to idols. It may have felt like a denial of Christ for them. So, Paul reminded the church that love should trump their freedom to eat meat.

Sacrificial love is needed in our churches today. Freedom in Christ is a delicate balance. While we are free to enjoy many things, we must consider if abstaining from certain things would be the more loving choice. Have you been in a situation where you felt free to enjoy something that a sister or brother in Christ felt convicted about? Is there an area where perhaps you need to abstain out of love for them?

S—The S stands for *Scripture*

O—The O stands for *Observation*

A—The A stands for *Application*

K—The K stands for *Kneeling in Prayer*

Do you not know

that in a race all the runners run,

but only one receives the prize?

So run that you may obtain it.

1 Corinthians 9:24

Reflection Question:

The Corinthians were familiar with the ancient Olympic Games. So, Paul used the example of both a runner and a boxer to show the way in which we as believers must live our Christian life. Winners are not slackers. Winners work and train hard to obtain the prize.

Paul tells us to put effort into living the Christian life and into sharing the gospel. We should live just like an athlete that competes to win. There is a reward awaiting us in heaven. We are to run hard and fight hard. Are you living your Christian life in this way? What is one thing that you need to change so you can run more effectively?

1 Corinthians 9

S—The S stands for *Scripture*

O—The O stands for *Observation*

A—The A stands for *Application*

K—The K stands for *Kneeling in Prayer*

Whether you eat or drink,

or whatever you do,

do all to the glory of God.

1 Corinthians 10:31

Reflection Question:

Paul warned the Corinthian church against idolatry and also against taking advantage of their Christian liberties. All things may be lawful but are they helpful? We are not to seek our own good but rather the good of our neighbor. This takes great maturity, wisdom, sensitivity and sacrificial love. Whatever we do, we must do to the glory of God.

God has given us great freedom and he wants us to enjoy all the good things he has created for us. But we must never forget how our freedoms affect our neighbors. God does not want us caught up in legalism and man-made rules, yet there are times when we must lay down our rights and liberties, out of love for our neighbor. Sacrificial love is so needed in the church today, but more freedom is also needed in the church today as well. Which way do you tend to swing, towards legalism or towards freedom? Is there an area in your life where it would be more loving for you to do something different?

1 Corinthians 10

S—The S stands for *Scripture*

O—The O stands for *Observation*

A—The A stands for *Application*

K—The K stands for *Kneeling in Prayer*

For anyone who eats and drinks

without discerning the body

eats and drinks judgment on himself.

1 Corinthians 11:29

Reflection Question:

The Lord's Supper was causing division in the Corinthian church. Paul explained that they were taking it irreverently and selfishly. That is a dangerous thing to do. He called on them to examine themselves before they took of the cup and bread or they would face discipline from the Lord.

The Lord's Supper is not a fancy meal. It is simple and it is meant to be done as an act of worship and remembrance of Christ's body and blood shed for our sin. First, are you regularly participating in the Lord's Supper? If not, begin this week to find a local church to join. Secondly, if you are taking the Lord's Supper regularly, examine yourself. In what manner have you been taking it? Is there anything you need to change?

1 Corinthians 11

S—The S stands for *Scripture*

O—The O stands for *Observation*

A—The A stands for *Application*

K—The K stands for *Kneeling in Prayer*

If one member suffers,

all suffer together.

1 Corinthians 12:26

Reflection Question:

Every single believer has been given a gift from the Holy Spirit. Spiritual gifts are not given for self-glorification but to glorify God and to build up the body of Christ. Love is the goal of the spiritual gifts.

Church is not a place we attend once a week to fill a seat and then leave. The Church is meant to function as a body. If one part is hurting, we all should hurt. Spiritual gifts are very practical in nature. They are to be used to care for one another just like we care for our little toe when we stub it or our eye when it is hurting. This is why divisions and fighting in the church so displease the Lord. God wants us to have a loving heart towards one another. Do you know what your spiritual gift is? How are you using it to love those in your church? If you don't know, pray and ask the Lord to show you.

1 Corinthians 12

S—The S stands for *Scripture*

O—The O stands for *Observation*

A—The A stands for *Application*

K—The K stands for *Kneeling in Prayer*

So now faith, hope, and love abide,

but the greatest of these is love.

1 Corinthians 13:13

Reflection Question:

While our spiritual gifts are wonderful, it is faith, hope and love that we all must pursue. All of the New Testament speaks to the pursuit of these but the greatest of the these is love. Love trumps faith, hope and our spiritual gifts. Without love, our gifts are useless. One day when we see Jesus and we will no longer need faith or hope. But we will experience love for all of eternity!

In 1 Corinthians 13, love is not defined as a feeling but rather as an action. Love is not fragile, and it is not proud. It is humble and it endures forever. Read 1 Corinthians 13:4-8 and evaluate yourself. In what ways do you need to be more loving to those closest to you and to those in your church?

1 Corinthians 13

S—The S stands for *Scripture*

O—The O stands for *Observation*

A—The A stands for *Application*

K—The K stands for *Kneeling in Prayer*

For God is not a God of confusion

but of peace.

1 Corinthians 14:33

Reflection Question:

Paul was reminding the Corinthian church that all worship and use of spiritual gifts should be done in an orderly way and for the edification of all believers. Also, they were not to just passively receive a word of encouragement. He wanted them to participate and give as well. The goal is that we all learn and are all encouraged.

God wants us to yield the use of our spiritual gift to the Spirit's leading. We are not to selfishly use our gift whenever we feel like it. This can lead to confusion and disorder. If you have been in the church long, most likely you have seen someone cause disorder in the church because they were asserting themselves and their desires. How can you avoid being the person who causes this? Write a prayer below asking God to guide you as you use your spiritual gifts.

1 Corinthians 14

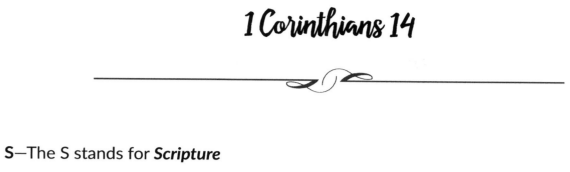

S—The S stands for *Scripture*

O—The O stands for *Observation*

A—The A stands for *Application*

K—The K stands for *Kneeling in Prayer*

Be steadfast, immovable,

always abounding in the work of the Lord,

knowing that in the Lord

your labor is not in vain.

1 Corinthians 15:58

Reflection Question:

Because death has been swallowed up in victory and we have a hope of resurrection with Christ, we can stand firm. We can be immovable. We can work hard serving the Lord knowing that all of our labor is not in vain. There is a sure hope of eternal life with Jesus one day!

Do you have days when you are weary from serving the Lord, that you are tempted to feel like maybe it's not worth it? How does remembering the truth of our future resurrection with Jesus, help you to not give up and to abound in the work of the Lord?

1 Corinthians 15

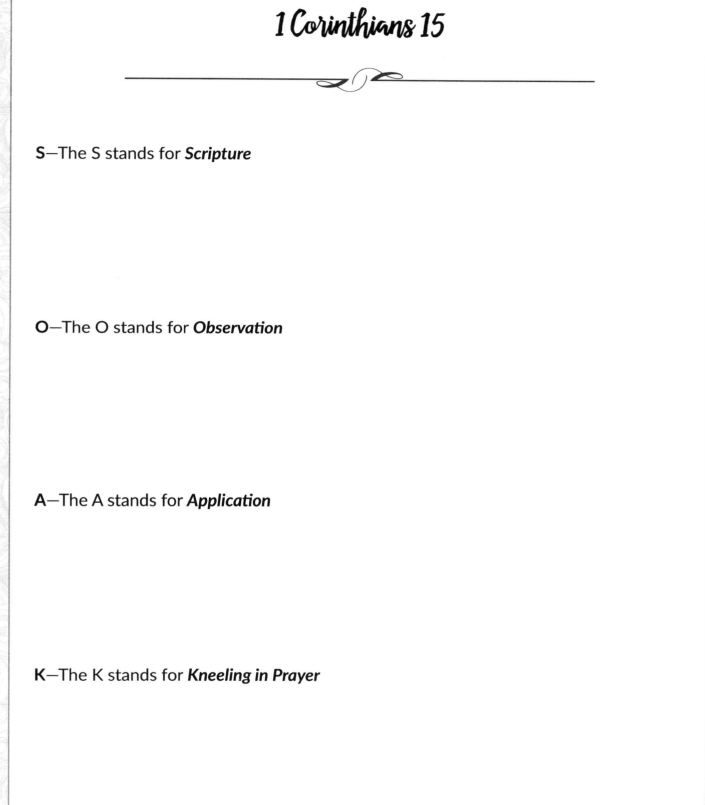

S—The S stands for *Scripture*

O—The O stands for *Observation*

A—The A stands for *Application*

K—The K stands for *Kneeling in Prayer*

Let all that you do

be done in love.

1 Corinthians 16:14

Reflection Question:

The Corinthian church needed clarity on many issues inside the church that were causing divisions. As Paul closes out his letter, he reminds them one last time to seek to do everything out of a heart of love for one another.

This is the same message we need in our churches today. There would be so much less division in our churches, if we would simply let all that we do, be done in love. In what ways can you show more love inside of your church? Write a prayer below asking God to help you apply all that you have learned through the book of 1 Corinthians in your life.

S—The S stands for *Scripture*

O—The O stands for *Observation*

A—The A stands for *Application*

K—The K stands for *Kneeling in Prayer*

Made in the USA
San Bernardino, CA
19 August 2019